R-MAN

FIERCEST FOES

Writer
Fred Van Lente
Artist
Cory Hamscher
with Terry Pallot
Colors
Guru eFX
Letters
Dave Sharpe
Cover Art: **Patrick Scherberger, Norman Lee
& Guru eFX; Francis Tsai; and David Nakayama,
Gary Martin & Guru eFX**
Assistant Editor: **Nathan Cosby**
Editor: **Mark Paniccia**

Collection Editor: **Jennifer Grünwald**
Assistant Editors: **Cory Levine & John Denning**
Editor, Special Projects: **Mark D. Beazley**
Senior Editor, Special Projects: **Jeff Youngquist**
Senior Vice President of Sales: **David Gabriel**
Vice President of Creative: **Tom Marvelli**

Editor in Chief: **Joe Quesada**
Publisher: **Dan Buckley**

#33

Days later...

Can't get Aunt May's words out of my *head*...maybe she's *right*, as usual!

After all...what's the *point* of me being *Spider-Man* if I can't change the world for the better...for *good?*

I don't want to be some *costumed street cleaner,* throwing the same crooks back into jail over and over and *over* again...

If Ock *has* reformed, he deserves a chance at a *normal* life.

STARK I

COMPANY PICNIC 2
—FLUSHING MEADOWS

A regular job *here*, at the Stark International plant...

Go on the *company picnic* like.

Wow. Like *everybody,* I guess.

There's not a single *light* o in that pla--

Wait

just

a minute..

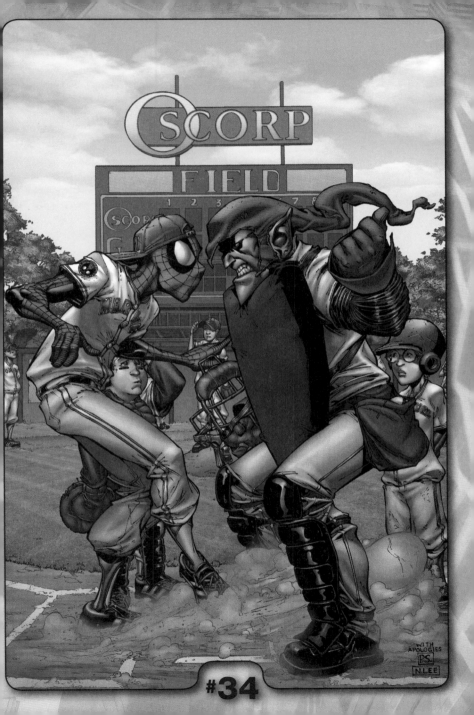

#35

BITTEN BY AN IRRADIATED SPIDER, WHICH GRANTED HIM INCREDIBLE ABILITIES, **PETER PARKER** LEARNED THE ALL-IMPORTANT LESSON, THAT WITH GREAT POWER THERE MUST ALSO COME GREAT RESPONSIBILITY. AND SO HE BECAME THE AMAZING **SPIDER-MAN**

Help! HELLLLP!

I'm being *mugged!*

The SIDE-KICK

FRED VAN LENTE
WRITER

CORY HAMSCHER
WITH **TERRY PALLOT**
ART

GURU eFX
COLORS

DAVE SHARPE
LETTERS

FRANCIS TSAI
COVER

ANTHONY DIAL
PRODUCTION

NATHAN COSBY
ASST. EDITOR

MARK PANICCIA
EDITOR

JOE QUESADA
EDITOR IN CHIEF

DAN BUCKLEY
PUBLISHER

That *mean* something to you?

Maybe... I'm seeing a *pattern* here.

Looks like these goofs just boosted solid silver *tea services* from *Northeby's Auction House*, down the block!

This gang is dressed like the Mad Hatter, the March Hare and the Dormouse...

...all of whom attended the *Mad Tea Party* in Lewis Carroll's *Alice in Wonderland!*

I *loved* Carroll as a kid... had all his books *memorized!*

Those *card nuts* earlier tonight were robbing a *molasses magnate.*

Another word for molasses is *"treacle"*--that's a major part of the Mad Tea Party, too!

On my *signal:* One... *two...*

Holy *Themed Thieveries,* S.M.!

This *library robbery* could be part of the same *bookworm crime spree!*

We'd better investigate *Lethally!*

Don't call me S.M.

OOF!

#36

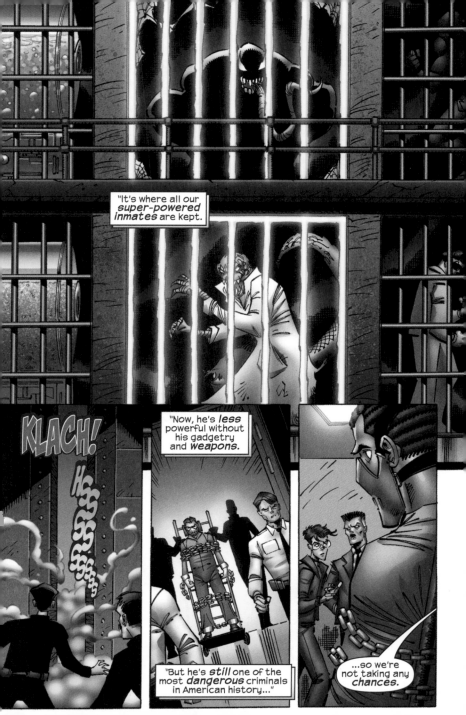

"It's where all our *super-powered inmates* are kept.

"Now, he's *less* powerful without his gadgetry and *weapons.*

KLACH!

HSSSSSS

"But he's *still* one of the most *dangerous* criminals in American history..."

...so we're not taking any *chances.*

KRAKKATHOOOM!

So much for *reinforce-ments.*

You've got to get me *out* of here! Do you know how valuable my *life* is?!

To New York's Boldest, *all* human life is valuable, sir--

You see?! That's why you're not *rich!*

Actually, the guards will still get *one* reinforce-ment...

...let's hope he's *enough!*

The End